Sesame Street Playground

Written by Sarah Albee
Illustrated by Tom Brannon

Reader's Digest Young Families

Oh, dear! A little black puppy was lost, and Elmo just had to find him. Elmo searched the neighborhood until he heard cheers coming from the Sesame Street Playground. He stopped a minute to watch some monsters practice for a baseball game. Suddenly, the puppy appeared and scooped up the ball.

"Get that puppy!" cried the players.

The players started to run after the puppy.
Elmo worried that the puppy would be scared.
"Quick, everyone!" he called to his friends.
"Help Elmo keep those monsters busy so they
won't chase the puppy."

"Excuse me, Mr. Angry-Looking Monster, sir!" called Grover to a passing monster. "Please show an adorable blue monster a little kindness! Give me just a teensy-tiny push so I can swing."

So the monster did.

"Hello, Mr. Monster!" called Elmo to a player from the red team. "Would you please lift Elmo up to these monkey bars?"

So the monster did.

"Helloooooo!" Zoe called to a player from the blue team. "It's a long way to slide! Would you please catch me at the bottom?"

So the monster did.

"Hi there!" Big Bird called from the sandbox. "Would you help me dig some sand for my castle, please?"

So the monsters did.

"Yoo-hoo!" called Prairie Dawn from the seesaw. "We need someone to sit on the other end so we can balance. Please sit there!"

So the monster did.

"Hey!" he called to all his friends. "This playground is fantastic! Let's just forget about the game and stay here and play!"

The baseball players agreed. So they all stayed and played.

And that was a lucky thing for the little black puppy.

Elmo's Everyday Words

balance

To make one thing equal to another in some way.
How many twiddlebugs would it take to balance you?

A game played by two teams that take turns hitting a ball with a bat and trying to score runs.
What other games need a ball?

baseball

dig

To make holes in dirt and move it around; also to look for something that's been hidden.
What things do you find when you dig?

To raise something up. The safe way to lift heavy things is to bend your knees, not your back.
What things do you lift?

lift

lucky

Having good things happen. People think some objects, like horseshoes, are lucky charms.
Count the leaves on this clover!

To be part of a game, to move around, or to just have fun; also to make music.
How do you play?

play

playground

A place outdoors where kids can play safely. Some have swings, slides, and seesaws.
What's in your playground?

To move quickly on foot. It's fun to run when you race or play games where you chase someone, like tag.
Where do you like to run?

run

slide

To move smoothly on a surface. A slide is also a thing. You slide down slides at the playground.
What other things slide?

To move back and forth, as on a swing; to move a bat, as in playing baseball.
How do you make swings move?

swing

team

A group of people that play or work together. Players on a team help each other to do their best.
Who's on your dream team?

Big Bird's BIG Ideas

practice

To do something over and over to get better at it. Teams do drills; dancers rehearse steps; you practice reading and writing.
What would you like to do better?

kindness

A good deed or favor; wanting to do nice things for others. You can show kindness in many ways: by helping out, by being polite, even just by smiling or listening. Can you think of more ways to be kind?

fantastic

Something almost beyond one's imagination; also a way of saying "Great!" when something good happens. **What words do you use when you're happy or excited?**

neighborhood

The people and places that are near where you live. Some neighborhoods have playgrounds or other places where kids can play together. Where do you go to play with friends?